MY FUN WITH
READING

◆

Stories About
Space and Earth Science

MY FUN WITH
READING

BOOK 5

Stories About
Space and Earth Science

SERIES EDITOR
Ronald Kidd

READING CONSULTANTS
Paul E. Stanton, Ph.D.
University of South Carolina, Coastal Carolina College

Ann Lukasevich, Ed.D.
University of British Columbia

THE SOUTHWESTERN COMPANY ■ NASHVILLE, TENNESSEE

RONALD KIDD is owner and Editorial Director of Kidd & Company, Inc., a Nashville-based packager and producer of children's books and records. Previously he held positions as Creative Director, Walt Disney Records, and Editor, Bowmar/Noble Publishers. The published author of seventeen books, he was recipient of the Children's Choice Award, the CINE Golden Eagle, and two Gold Records. He has been nominated for the Edgar Allan Poe Award, the Grammy Award, and the California Young Reader Medal. Mr. Kidd has a secondary teaching credential in English and history.

DR. PAUL E. STANTON completed his Ph.D. at the University of South Carolina in the field of Counseling Psychology, with an emphasis in reading and learning disabilities. He chaired the Department of Reading and Language Arts at the University of Pittsburgh and was co-chair of the Committee on Undergraduate Training in the Teaching of Reading for the International Reading Association (IRA). He was co-developer of the Scholastic *Action* Series, a pioneer high-interest/low-ability reading series produced by Scholastic Book Services. Dr. Stanton served as Vice Chancellor for Academic Affairs at the University of South Carolina, Coastal Carolina College, where he is currently Professor of Psychology specializing in reading and learning disabilities.

DR. ANN LUKASEVICH taught for seventeen years at the elementary school level in Ontario, Canada. She is presently a member of the Language Department at the University of British Columbia, where she originally obtained her Ed.D., and teaches courses in language, reading, early childhood, and curriculum development. She also taught reading and language courses at the University of Calgary for one year and at the University of Western Ontario for three years. During this period, she has done numerous workshops and conference presentations in early childhood education, reading, and language in Canada and the United States. She spent a year in Britain studying British education, and was awarded an advanced Diploma in Child Development. Her interests include parent involvement, evaluation, literacy development, and computer education.

SERIES DESIGN   Bruce Gore
PAGE DESIGN AND ART PRODUCTION   Schatz + Schatz
COVER PHOTOS   NASA (top)
                  Stephen McBrady (center and bottom)

CONTENTS

Journey to the Edge of
SPACE

by CYNTHIA A. HILL and LUANNE C. BOLE-BECKER

If you need help
with hard words,
please turn to p. 36.

PHOTOGRAPHS:

Courtesy Challenger Center for Space Science Education pp. 9, 10, 11 (bottom), 13-22, 23 (bottom), 27-29, 33, 34, 36
Courtesy National Aeronautics and Space Administration (NASA) pp. 7, 11 (top), 23 (top), 24, 30, 32

ILLUSTRATIONS: Joel Snyder

We gratefully acknowledge the cooperation of the Challenger Center for Space Science Education.

The clock was ticking. Launch time was six minutes away, but the crew members aboard the space station *Legacy* sat calmly in front of their stations, absorbed in their work.

Around the room, the shiny control panels flashed and buzzed. The talk of the busy crew hummed over the click of switches, the whine of motors, and the tapping of computer keys.

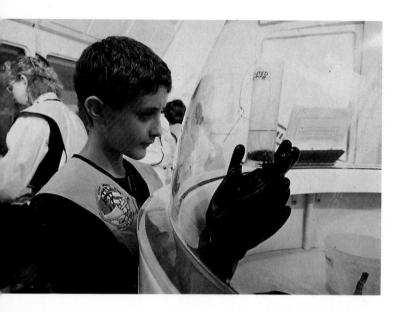

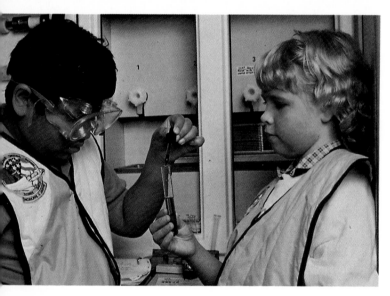

In the center of the room, a remote team member, arms thrust into black rubber gloves in a clear dome, analyzed soil samples. Off to one side, the life support team peered at the murky contents of a test tube. In a glass-enclosed area, another team assembled sections of a probe, about to be launched into the tail of Comet Halley. Its purpose — to send back information about our universe.

Nearby, a viewing screen showed clouds swirling above the globe of the Earth. Far beneath the clouds, on the Earth's surface, was mission control. There, team members checked their monitors to make sure things were going smoothly on the space station.

Sarah, one of the life support team, stared in shock at her monitor. "Tim," she called to a teammate, "if these numbers are right, the entire space station crew is in *trouble*!"

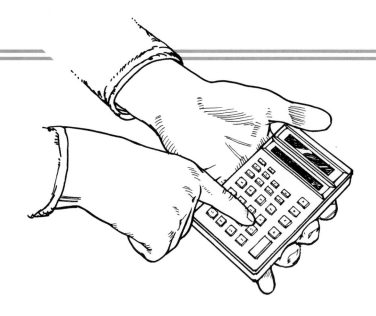

Tim's stool screeched as he rushed to join her. "Why? What's wrong?"

"See these figures?" said Sarah, pointing to her screen. "They measure oxygen pressure in the cabin." She punched in a set of numbers on her calculator. "It's way too low for a crew of sixteen!"

Tim tapped at his calculator. "I sure hope it's a computer error, or in about four minutes the crew will start to lose consciousness."

"Which means we have only three minutes to figure this out!" Sarah said. She scribbled a message for Ben. Known as "CapCom," he handled communications for mission control.

Ben tried to keep his voice calm as he contacted "SimCom," the specialist in communications on board space station *Legacy.* "CapCom to SimCom. I have an urgent message. Over."

A voice crackled over the little speaker on Ben's control panel. "SimCom to CapCom. We are ready to receive. Over."

"The computer shows dangerously low oxygen levels on board. Are you picking up any problems on your oxygen flow display? Over." As they waited for a response, Sarah and Tim looked at the monitors to keep track of the time.

It was only last night that Sarah was looking up into the inky sky, wondering why she had been chosen for life support. After all, space flight and its support had always been an adventure for adults. And Sarah's own adulthood seemed as far away as those tiny stars above her. Yet here she was in the year 2061, responsible for the health and safety of an entire crew as they readied themselves for a rendezvous with Comet Halley.

Comet Halley

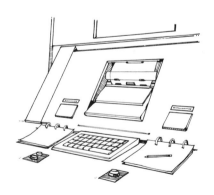

The little speaker hissed back to life. "SimCom to CapCom. I have a message for life support. Do you read me? Over."

"Life support is ready to receive," said Ben. "Over."

"Our computers are showing a leak in valve number one, and the number three opening is stuck in the off position. Can you advise? Over."

Advise? Sarah could only shrug her shoulders. "Ben, I have to get the flight director. Can you tell *Legacy* we're working on it?"

Sarah quickly explained the problem to the flight director. "I'm sorry, Sarah," he said, "but I don't think I can help you."

He put a reassuring hand on her shoulder. "I know you can solve this problem, Sarah. The whole crew's depending on you. Besides," he added, "you come so very highly recommended." As he walked away, Sarah's stomach turned a somersault.

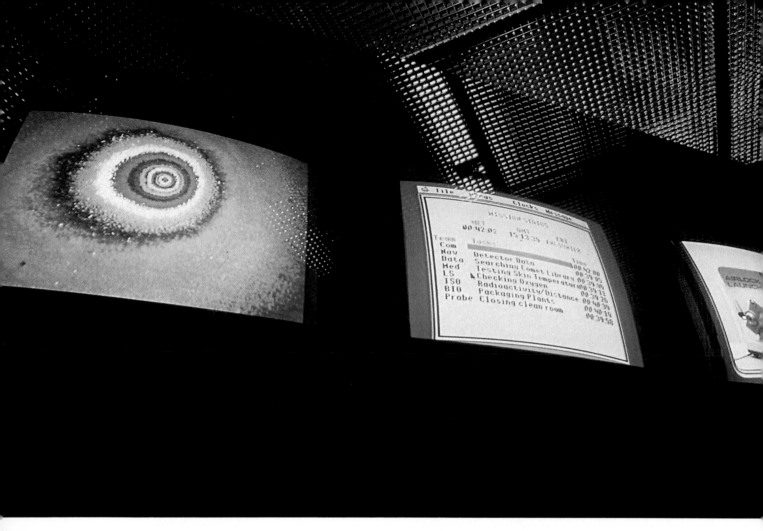

Ben and Tim looked up eagerly as she returned. Sarah swallowed hard, then asked, "Tim, will you figure out how much oxygen is needed for the crew size? I need more information."

She wrote out another message. Ben read it into the microphone. "CapCom to SimCom. Life support controllers need close-up visuals of your oxygen flow display. Can you provide? Over."

"Roger, CapCom. We are positioning the camera now. Over."

Instantly, red and green lights dotted the video screen. At first it was only a jumble of boxes, tubes, and numbered lights. Sarah sat in front of the monitor with her chin in her hands. How was she supposed to make sense of this in just two minutes? She tried to concentrate.

"Now if this route is leaking," she mumbled, "we have to close this section off. And that valve is stuck shut, so we have to find another passage — maybe through there."

To Sarah's growing amazement, a pattern began to emerge. She sketched out her ideas, closing off some valves and opening others. Sarah sat back and stared at her plan. She had just plotted a brand new path for the oxygen! Tim added his calculations to her diagram, and she handed it to Ben.

Oxygen flow diagram

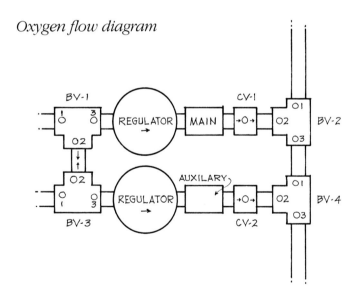

"CapCom to SimCom," said Ben. "We are sending you a diagram of the revised oxygen flow. It shows which new valves to activate. Pressure settings are also included. Please advise us of your progress. Over."

Ben and Sarah looked up at the mission status monitor. If the probe wasn't launched in exactly four minutes, the *Legacy* would miss the precise launch angle calculated by the navigation team.

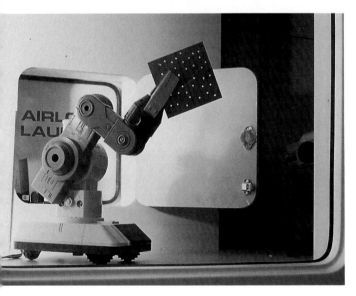

The speaker buzzed with the background chatter of the *Legacy* crew.

Then: "SimCom to CapCom. Oxygen system is repaired! Thanks for your help. Over." Ben hooted and gave Sarah and Tim a high five.

As Sarah and her teammates went back to their monitors, work on board the *Legacy* continued. The comet's location was verified. One of the monitors showed holes in the meteoroid shield, and a robot was sent to get it.

Assembling the probe

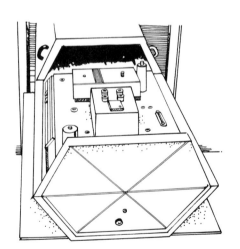

One of the space station's cameras was trained on the probe team as they assembled the last components of the device. If the probe went off course, scientists would have to wait another seventy-six years for Comet Halley to come close enough for another try.

The mission commander walked up to the cabin microphone. "Attention, *Legacy* crew. There are two minutes left to comet rendezvous. Please finish your jobs and close up your stations."

The probe team bent over the probe's metal casing as they plugged in the last few pieces of equipment. A team member pushed in the sliding drawer to ready the probe for launch. The one-minute countdown began.

"...Five, four, three, two, one, ignition."

A black metal bar locked into place over the probe drawer. All eyes moved to the flight monitor. A single light flashed across the screen as scanners tracked the path of the probe. It sped straight into the tail of Comet Halley!

The probe began sending data and photos to the space station with lightning speed. At the same time, three glass tubes at the front of the cabin began to fill with gases. Using special glasses, the crew could see the colorful spectral signatures of the gases found in the comet's tail.

*Comet approaching
Earth's orbit*

Back at mission control, Sarah listened excitedly as news of the probe came over the speaker. "SimCom to CapCom. Probe launch was successful. The station is about to shut down. We're coming home."

Future NASA mission launching probe into comet

"Welcome back," announced the mission commander, "to the 1990s. You have just successfully completed your simulated mission to Comet Halley. The events that you experienced were based on past and future NASA missions. And even though *simulation* means the trip wasn't real, your teamwork certainly was!"

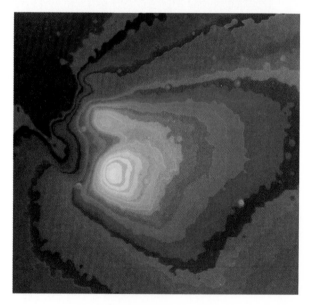

Picture of Comet Halley taken with special camera. Different colors show different amounts of light, from white to black. Nucleus, or head of comet, is dark area at upper left.

The simulated mission to Comet Halley, set in the year 2061, is reenacted day after day at special sites called Challenger Learning Centers. Housed in museums, science centers, and schools across the nation, each center includes a space station interior and mission control room. In these settings, students and teachers work side by side in teams. Together they learn to solve math, science, and technology problems during a mock space flight.

The simulated space flights and Challenger Learning Centers are just one part of a broad program sponsored by the Challenger Center for Space Science Education. Founded by the seven families of the *Challenger* astronauts, it was created to carry on the unique educational mission of the original crew.

When the space shuttle *Challenger* soared into flight on January 28, 1986, students across the nation were watching. Most knew that the crew included the nation's first teacher-in-space, Christa McAuliffe.

Many had prepared for a week of lessons from space. In these lessons, each of the astronauts would conduct in-flight studies about the future space station. *Challenger* also carried a number of experiments designed by school children.

Launch of Challenger shuttle (January 28, 1986)

Challenger crew: (seated l-r) *Astronauts Michael J. Smith, Francis R. Scobee, Ronald E. McNair;* (standing, l-r) *Astronaut Ellison S. Onizuka, Teacher-in-Space Christa McAuliffe, Payload Specialist Gregory Jarvis, Astronaut Judith A. Resnik*

Then came the tragic shuttle explosion, leaving the crew's mission undone. Months later, the families of the astronauts joined together and vowed to complete a vital part of the *Challenger* mission: "To teach, to explore, to inspire." Thus, Challenger Center was born.

What has evolved is a powerful network of people, places, and programs. These programs include teacher workshops, classroom teleconferences, and simulated space flights such as Sarah's.

Teacher workshop

Classroom teleconference

Astronaut Edwin E. Aldrin, Jr.,
walking on moon

It's been over twenty years since the first people walked on the moon. Much progress has been made since then, but there's still a long way to go. Who will be the first person to *live* on the moon? To walk on Mars? To explore the satellites of Jupiter? It all depends on the young people of today.

Exploring the satellites
of Jupiter

The grass prickled the backs of Sarah's legs as she looked up into the night sky. She could still see the smile on her teacher's face when Sarah came to class the next day.

"Well, mission control," Mrs. Rhodes had said. "Was the launch a success?"

Sarah had explained how she found a new path for the crew's oxygen flow. Mrs. Rhodes didn't seem the least surprised.

"And the flight director said I came very highly recommended!" laughed Sarah. "You'd think I'd just graduated from Star Fleet Academy!" There was a brightness in Mrs. Rhodes's eyes that Sarah had never noticed before.

"Mrs. Rhodes?" asked Sarah. "How come you look like you already knew all this?"

Mrs. Rhodes laughed. "I've always known about your strong problem-solving abilities, Sarah. I'm just pleased that now you know about them, too!"

Sarah looked up into the sky. Why did the stars look different tonight? Certainly they were brighter. But how odd, she thought, that some stars should look closer than the night before. That big one by the moon — that must be a planet. As Sarah thought about her journey to the edge of space, she reached up one arm toward the bright star. A little farther now, she thought, and I can just about touch it.

What Does It Mean?

absorbed: paying close attention

murky: cloudy

probe: a craft sent into space to send back data or information

reassure: to make (someone) feel better

recommend: to suggest

reenact: to act or perform again

remote: far away

retrieve: to bring back

revise: to change, with the goal of improving

satellite: a body that circles or orbits another body

teleconference: a meeting of people far apart who are brought together by TV

vital: of the greatest importance

How Do You Say It?

calculations: kal kyuh LAY shuns

consciousness: KAHN shuh sness

meteroid: MEET ee uh roid

navigation: nah vih GAY shun

oxygen: AHK sih jen

rendezvous: RAHN day voo

spectral signature: SPEC trull SIG nuh cher

technology: tek NOLL uh jee

Painting
THE PAST

by RONALD KIDD

*If you need help
with hard words,
please turn to p. 66.*

PHOTOGRAPHS: Stephen McBrady

ILLUSTRATIONS: Mark Hallett

All illustrations ©Mark Hallett, except pp. 46-47 and 60 (bottom) by Mark Hallett for *Ranger Rick's Dinosaur Book,* ©1984 by the National Wildlife Federation

We gratefully acknowledge the cooperation of the George C. Page Museum of La Brea Discoveries, a satellite of the Natural History Museum of Los Angeles County.

ARTIST'S DEDICATION: To my dear Veronica, who helped make this all possible.

It looks like an ordinary house. Tucked behind shade trees on a quiet street, it has a big wooden door with shuttered windows on each side. The neatly trimmed yard is bordered by low shrubs and flowers. Every once in a while, people stroll by. Most of them don't even notice the place.

A car pulls into the driveway, and a man gets out. He unlocks the front door and goes inside. A moment later he walks into the backyard.

It's as if he stepped into another world.

There are wild grasses and boulders. Trees arch over a small, rugged canyon. The sounds of traffic are gone, replaced by a breeze blowing through the branches. The man follows a path that winds among the boulders. With each step he leaves the modern world farther behind.

Off to one side, a cat pads silently through the grass. The cat stops, eyes glued to a robin. The man watches, then sits on a rock and opens a sketchpad. With a few quick strokes he draws the arch of the cat's back, the angle of its legs, the glitter in its eyes.

"Heather," he calls. The cat turns to look at him, and the robin flutters away. "Time to go to work."

The man closes his sketchpad. With Heather following, he makes his way into a low building set back among the trees. It's a cozy place, crowded with strange objects. There are skulls and fossils and animal pelts. There are brushes, paints, and a drawing board.

This building is the man's office, and these are his tools. What kind of job does he have? In this small studio on a quiet suburban street, Mark Hallett brings dinosaurs to life.

As a young boy, Mark loved going to the museum. He was especially fascinated by fossils — remains of plants and animals from the past. His friends would look at dinosaur fossils and see old bones. Mark would look beyond the bones and try to imagine what the creatures looked like. Did they have skin? Did they have scales, like crocodiles? What color were they? Where did they live? How did they move?

Years ago in the western United States, there were lush plains and forests along river beds. Many types of dinosaurs lived there. Their bones were sometimes buried in river sand during floods, saving them for us to find today.

Triceratops *was one of the newest dinosaurs to appear and perhaps one of the last to become extinct. Its powerful beak was used for chopping tough vegetation. The beak could also have been used as a weapon against* Tyrannosaurus *and other meat-eating dinosaurs.*

Sometimes Mark will draw an animal in several different positions to help understand its shape and bring the animal to life, as in these drawings of the North American dinosaur Tenontosaurus.

SHADOW OVER LEFT THREE
TENONTOSAURS TO THROW INTO
FOREGROUND.

TENONTOSAURUS

People who study fossils are called *paleontologists.* Mark thought of becoming one, but he also wanted a career as an artist. He attended art school, where he worked on children's books, fashion magazines, and technical projects. While he worked, he dreamed of dinosaurs. He longed to bring them back to life. And he thought that through his art, he might be able to do just that.

After graduating, Mark did some packaging and magazine illustrations. Then one day a publisher called. "Mark," he said, "we need some paintings for a magazine article. Have you ever thought about drawing dinosaurs?"

He'd been waiting a long time for someone to ask him that question.

The project went well, and word spread. Before Mark knew it, he had the career he had hoped for. He was a paleo-artist. His job was to work with paleontologists and other experts in recreating plants and animals of the past, through painted pictures.

Today Mark is beginning a new assignment. The George C. Page Museum in Los Angeles has asked him to do paintings of an extinct sabertoothed cat that lived in California many years ago. Let's follow the project to see what a paleo-artist does.

In danger from a meat-eating Ceratosaurus, *a young* Stegosaurus *fights for its life with its spiked tail*.

Such tails could probably strike upwards and sideways with great accuracy at the head of an attacking dinosaur.

The first step is reading — lots of it. Mark gets all the best books and scientific papers he can find on sabertoothed cats. He studies text and diagrams, taking careful notes.

Next he contacts a leading expert at a museum or university. In this case Mark is learning about the shape and structure of the cat's skull. He is especially interested in the workings of the jaw. How far did it open? How did the cat bite? Details such as this are important if Mark's paintings are to be accurate and lifelike.

At this stage he likes to get a first-hand look at the fossils. The Page Museum is built over tar pits in which animals were trapped many years ago. As a result, the museum has a fine collection of sabertoothed-cat bones. Mark spends several hours sketching and taking pictures of the cat's bone structure.

His next stop is the museum lab. Here, bones are cleaned, labeled, and stored in metal drawers.

Mark talks to the lab manager about the shape of the paws. He studies the paw bones through a magnifying glass and makes more sketches. He even measures the bones, trying to learn exactly what the paws looked like and how they worked.

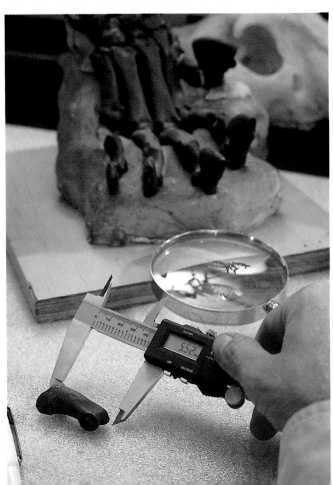

Rapator was an Australian meat-eating dinosaur, a relative of Allosaurus *from western North America. This action sketch was chosen as the body pose for the animal as it appears in the finished painting on pages 60-61.*

Many times, especially with dinosaurs, complete skeletons of the animal do not exist. In these cases, Mark studies the bones that are available and works with an expert to reconstruct the rest.

In this original research, Mark's work is not very different from that of a paleontologist. Mark likes to do his own research, however, because there have been times when the existing skeletons and drawings of an animal have turned out to be wrong.

The South American dinosaur Antarctosaurus

ANTARCTOSAURUS WICHMANNIANUS

Sometimes, in spite of all the research, there is not enough information to work with. Perhaps there are too few fossils, or too few ideas about how the bones fit together. In these cases, Mark does not try any paintings, since they would not be accurate.

When his research is finished, Mark goes back to his studio and begins drawing. He always starts with the animal's skeleton. This determines not only the shape of the body, but how the animal stood and moved. In this project Mark begins with the head of the sabertoothed cat, showing the jaw in opened and closed positions.

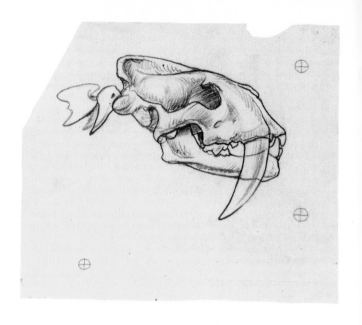

Once the skeleton drawings are finished, he moves on to the muscles. Unlike the hard bones, the muscles and other soft parts of these animals no longer exist. This is where the detective work begins.

Mark studies his clues. He can tell where some of the muscles were located because of scars or rough places on the bones. He then looks for similar marks on the bones of modern-day animals and might use the muscle structure of those animals as a model. He often talks with experts in animal motion, or *biomechanics*. Using all the clues he has gathered for this project, Mark draws the muscles of the sabertoothed cat.

Part of the Mark's job is to find out what extinct animals looked like. This process is called a restoration. *For his restoration of the sabertoothed cat, Mark started with a careful study and drawings of what was left of its skeleton. From those, he decided what the muscles and other soft parts were like, based on those of living relatives such as lions and tigers. Finally he gave it a covering of skin, fur, and whiskers. No one has ever found fur from a sabertooth, so we don't know whether it was spotted, striped, or one color. Mark thinks sabertooths had markings like bobcats. What do you think?*

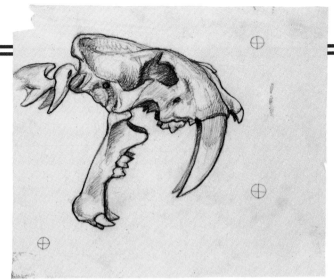

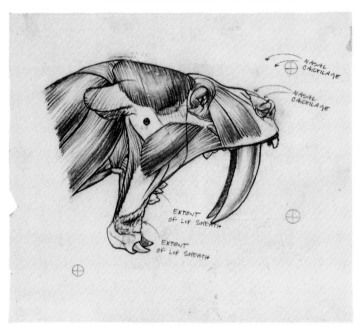

NASAL
CARTILAGE

NASAL
CARTILAGE

EXTENT
OF LIP SHEATH

EXTENT
OF LIP SHEATH

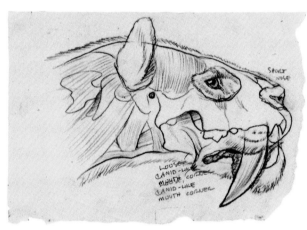

SHORT
NOSE

LOOSE
CANID-LIKE
MOUTH CORNER
CANID-LIKE
MOUTH CORNER

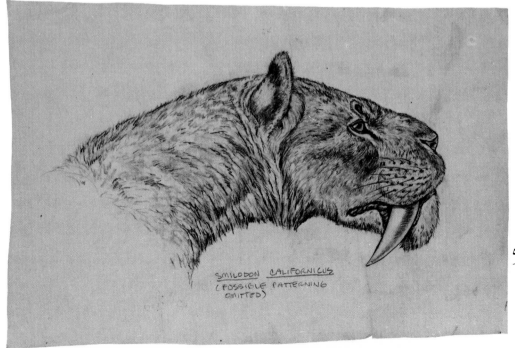

SMILODON CALIFORNICUS
(POSSIBLE PATTERNING
OMITTED)

55

His next drawing shows the skin or hide of the animal which covers the muscles. There is more detective work involved here. Again, some of his best clues come from similar modern-day animals. Mark studies pelts from these animals for fur color and texture. In the case of the sabertoothed cat, one of his sources of information was Heather!

Many modern animals rely on color and markings to help them blend into their environment. Mark feels that ancient animals could have done the same thing. Dinosaurs, for example, may not have been solid gray, brown, or green, as they are often shown. Instead, they might have had stripes or spots in any number of different colors, depending on where they lived.

At one time, few dinosaurs were known from Australia, but now several kinds have been discovered. There are also fossilized tracks showing where a group of plant-eating dinosaurs may have run from a meat eater.

At this stage, Mark's drawings show the subject on the page by itself. The next step is to show the animal in motion in its natural setting. For the sabertoothed cat project, he roams the areas where the great cats lived, taking pictures of the landscape. Then he goes back to his studio and sketches the cat in action, surrounded by the plants and animals of its day.

After finishing a restoration, Mark may follow with action sketches to get a feeling for the way the animal moved and lived. These may become "warm-up" drawings for a more detailed drawing or painting showing the animal in its environment. These sabertooth action sketches, along with the restoration, became the basis for the sabertooths in the painting on page 64.

Then and only then does Mark sit down at the drawing board and paint the scene he was hired to do. He uses everything he has learned about the sabertoothed cat — bone structure, muscles, fur, landscape, and motion — to create the finished piece. It might be only one painting, but it could represent weeks or even months of hard work.

Mark loves painting
ancient animals of all kinds,
but he finds himself
returning again and again
to dinosaurs.

*The dinosaurs died out,
leaving areas to small
mammals. Shown here
around a* Triceratops *skull
are* Eodidelphis (left),
Ptilodus, (center), *and*
Gobiaconodon (right) *with
its babies.*

One of the greatest scientific mysteries is why dinosaurs became extinct. One idea, or theory, *is that a giant meteorite struck the earth. This may have created tidal waves* (left), *a worldwide dust cloud, and volcanic eruptions that kept sunlight from reaching plants* (right). *As a result, many plants might have disappeared for a while, causing plant-eating dinosaurs and then meat-eating dinosaurs to die out* (center).

"I like them partly because they're so unusual," he says. "But unlike other exotic creatures such as dragons or unicorns, dinosaurs were real. In fact, for years they ruled the earth. Then suddenly, they were gone. What happened to them? No one really knows."

We do know a few things about them. There were many different types and sizes of dinosaur. Some were plant eaters *(herbivores),* while others were meat eaters *(carnivores).* Dinosaurs lived in virtually every corner of the world. It appears they migrated, much as whales do today, over hundreds or even thousands of miles.

Most people think dinosaurs were a type of lizard, but this is not true. In fact, their closest living relatives are birds. Some scientists even feel that dinosaurs may have had feathers! Again, no one knows for sure.

Mark's favorite dinosaurs are the gigantic sauropods, such as the long-necked *Mamenchisaurus.* Sauropods weighed fifty to sixty tons and stretched out to lengths of up to one hundred feet.

"It's hard to imagine that something so huge could disappear so completely," says Mark.

In western China, the remains of many new and strange dinosaurs are being found. One of them is Mamenchisaurus, *a relative of the giant* Apatosaurus *("Brontosaurus"), whose thirty-three-foot neck is the longest of any known animal.*

Chinese dinosaurs Omeisaurus *and* Yangchuanosaurus

This scene shows the plants and animals that lived in Southern California many years ago. Bones and other hard parts of creatures such as the sabertoothed cat Smilodon (center) *were covered and preserved by tar seeping out of cracks in the ground.*

Dinosaurs are extinct, but Mark points out that in our modern world, many animals and wilderness areas can still be saved. He feels that our destruction of the natural world is the most serious problem we face today.

Mark does what he can to preserve that world.

Young people find themselves attracted to his work because, like Mark, they want to see more than just bones. They want the creatures of the past to live and breathe.

And so Mark Hallett will go back into his studio, shut the door, and spend another afternoon in a world that is gone forever. With the help of Mark's paintings, you can join him there.

In the meantime, he continues to paint pictures of a more primitive world and its creatures. His work can be found in museums, books, magazines, posters, and calendars. He is currently a consulting artist for Paramount Pictures and Steven Spielberg, designing dinosaur characters for upcoming films.

What Does It Mean?

consulting artist: one who meets with others to help them draw things

diagram: a drawing that shows how something is built or put together

environment: living area or surroundings

extinct: no longer existing or living

flutter: to flap the wings quickly

magnifying glass: a rounded tool made of glass that makes things look bigger

migrate: to move from one area to another

pelt: the hair or fur of an animal, together with the skin beneath

primitive: of an early time or age

reconstruct: to put together again

skeleton: the bones or hard parts of an animal's body

virtually: almost, nearly

How Do You Say It?

available: uh VAY luh buhl

destruction: dih STRUCK shun

fascinated: FASS un ayt ed

gigantic: jie GAN tick

illustration: ill us TRAY shun

sabretoothed: SAY burr toothd

suburban: suh BURR bun

RECYCLING
With Sally

by ANN BRAYBROOKS

*If you need help
with hard words,
please turn to p. 96.*

PHOTOGRAPHS:

Stephen McBrady pp. 67-77, 80, 84, 89-96
Courtesy of Aluminum Company of America pp. 78, 79 (top left and right)
Glass Packaging Institute pp. 82, 83
Institute of Scrap Recycling Industries, Inc. p. 79 (bottom)
Southeast Paper Manufacturing Company pp. 85-87

ILLUSTRATIONS: Joel Snyder

We gratefully acknowledge the cooperation of the Burbank Recycling Center, Burbank, California.

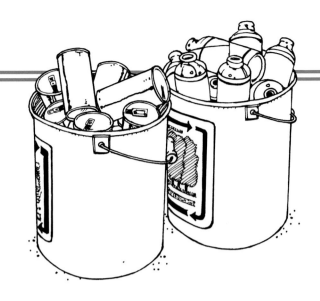

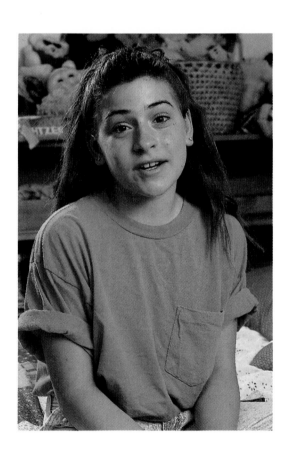

I admit that I'm a slob. Somehow I can't seem to pick up my clothes or put my books and tapes in order. I've got junk all over my room: empty soda cans, magazines, games. The mess really bothers my mom. I've been trying to tell her I'm only eleven years old and have the rest of my life to clean it up. She's not falling for it.

We just moved into a new neighborhood. Somehow I've messed up my new room, too. I promised to clean it up, but I needed a break after hanging up five pairs of jeans. So I grabbed a soda and the funnies from the paper, and I went outside.

"Hey," called a voice from across the yard, "may I have that can after you're done?" It was the girl who lived next door. I had seen her a week earlier, dragging two plastic buckets out to the curb. I'd been wondering what was in those buckets.

"I'm collecting stuff for the recycling center," she told me. "I've already filled one bucket with glass bottles. If you have more cans in your house, we could rinse them out and add them to the bucket for aluminum."

Then she added, "Hi, I'm Rosa Molina."

I told her my name was Sally Franklin and that we could go look inside. When she saw my bedroom, she laughed. "Your *room* should be recycled! If everybody treated the earth this way, the planet would be one huge trash heap."

"Hey, what's wrong with trash?" I said. "I've been collecting it for eleven years."

"Nothing, except there's so much of it that we're running out of places to put it. Did you know that the average American produces about 3½ pounds of garbage every day, which adds up to almost thirteen hundred pounds a year?"

"Who said?" I asked.

"My dad. He told me we should reuse things instead of throwing them away. That would save energy and natural resources, like the trees that are used to make paper.

"You know what?" she said. "Why don't you come to the recycling center with us? My dad organized a paper drive, and we're going to drop off the newspapers today."

I checked with my mom, then left with Rosa and her father for the recycling center. When we got there, Mr. Molina drove his pickup truck onto a scale where it was weighed with the newspapers — and us! — still in it. I learned this was called the *laden weight*.

After a computer showed the laden weight, we drove to a spot where we could unload the papers. Then the three of us got back into the truck, and Mr. Molina drove onto the scale again. While we were seated inside, Rosa's dad introduced us to the manager, Mr. Johnson.

We watched as Mr. Johnson subtracted the weight of the truck *without* papers from the weight *with* papers. The result was called the *net weight.* It would determine how much money the Molinas would get.

"Not every center pays for what you bring in," said Mr. Molina. "The important thing is to recycle, even if you don't get money for it."

Before we left the recycling center, Mr. Johnson offered to give Rosa and me a tour. He showed us where the aluminum cans were weighed in wire baskets, then dumped into a machine that flattened them. "Flattened or shredded cans take up less room," he explained, "which means we can ship a lot more cans at one time."

Stacks of aluminum cans and ingots at smelter

Molten aluminum being poured into ladle

Rosa asked, "What happens to the aluminum after it leaves the recycling center?"

"It's sent to a place called a *smelter*," Mr. Johnson said. "There, the aluminum is melted and purified. This liquid metal is poured into a ladle.

Then it's cooled, flattened, and rolled into coils. On a single machine, these coils are trimmed, leveled, washed, and coated. An inspector makes sure the coils are perfect before they're shipped to factories that make new cans."

Coils of aluminum being trimmed, leveled, washed, and coated

Inspector checking coils

Aluminum ingots

Mr. Johnson said the liquid metal is sometimes made into *ingots,* which look like metal bricks. These are also sent to aluminum can factories.

He added, "It takes only six weeks for a can to be recycled, from the time it comes to a recycling center to the time it appears again on a store shelf."

"Really?" said Rosa. "My dad never told me that. He did say that recycling aluminum saves ninety-five percent of the energy to produce new metal. The energy that's saved from recycling one can will run a TV for three hours!"

The Molinas sure seemed smart! But I admit I was having fun and learning a lot.

Next, Mr. Johnson told us about recycling glass. He said that glass bottles are weighed, then put into bins. These bins are taken by forklift to larger bins, called *roll-off containers*. Roll-off containers can be attached to a truck cab and driven to a processing center.

Cullet

Mr. Johnson showed us a roll-off container filled with bottles. As we stood beside it, he explained, "At the processing center, the glass is broken into little pieces, called *cullet*. The cullet is run through a machine that removes any metal pieces with an electromagnet."

"Great!" said Rosa. "That means we don't have to do it."

"That's right," said Mr. Johnson. "The clean cullet is screened and crushed, then mixed with sand, soda ash, and limestone. This mixture is heated in furnaces at about twenty-seven hundred degrees Fahrenheit until it melts.

*Automatic
bottle-forming
machine*

Then the molten, or liquid, glass is fed into automatic bottle-forming machines where it's shaped into containers. The bottles are cooled and then checked."

*Bottles being
cooled and checked*

Trying to sound smart, I asked, "And I suppose recycling glass saves energy, too?"

"Sure it does," said Mr. Johnson. "Recycled glass melts at a little bit lower temperature, reducing the amount of energy it takes to create new glass. Glass is one hundred percent recyclable. For every ton of used containers melted, a ton of new containers is produced."

Piles of old newspaper at mill

Next, Mr. Johnson offered to tell us about newspaper recycling. He walked us over to a big mound of papers. "First," he said, "used newspaper has to be taken by truck to a newsprint mill. There the papers are baled and stored, then dumped into piles that are much taller than this one."

Pulper

Washing ink from fibers

Rosa said, "I bet they look like newspaper hills!"

"They do," answered Mr. Johnson. "But not for long, because the newspaper is sent to something called a *pulper.* It works like a kitchen blender. As warm water is added, huge rotors stir the paper until it breaks down into pulp. Then chemicals are added which begin loosening the ink from the paper fibers."

Papermaking machine

Mr. Johnson said that once the ink is loosened, it is washed away from the fibers on large rotating cylinders with screens. Next it is fed into a papermaking machine, where most of the water is removed and the fibers are formed into a sheet of newsprint. The newsprint is rolled onto spools and inspected for quality, then wrapped for protection and shipped by truck or rail.

Newsprint rolls being inspected

"I don't want to sound rude," I said, "but instead of recycling, why can't we keep planting more trees?"

Mr. Johnson smiled. "We can't grow them fast enough! And like other types of recycling, reusing newspaper saves energy. It also cuts down on air pollution and the amount of garbage that's thrown away."

Rosa said, "It takes over half a million trees to give us our Sunday newspapers every week!"

I began to feel guilty about chopping down all those trees just to read the funnies. Rather than stop reading, I decided to start my own recycling program at home.

That afternoon, Mr. Johnson gave me plastic buckets for storing glass and aluminum. He told me to bundle the newspapers and stack them underneath the buckets when I brought them out to the curb once a week for pickup.

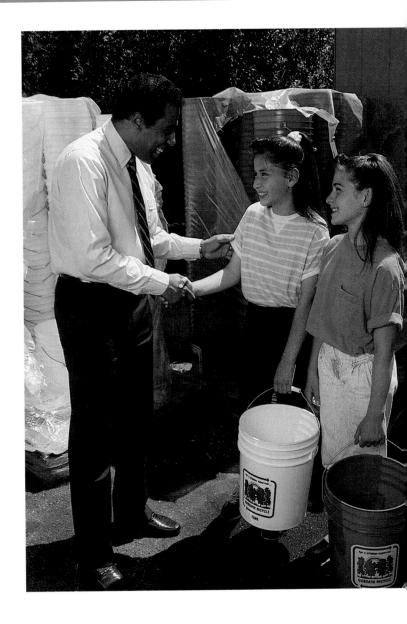

When I got home, I told my mom about my plan. She and I decided to place the buckets under the sink. Then I taped a sign above the sink for everyone to read. It said *Please rinse cans and bottles for recycling!* I thought we'd need this note until we got into the habit of sorting our trash. I also asked my dad to crush the cans so they took up less space.

Mr. Johnson had told me to store the newspapers in a clean, dry place, where there wouldn't be any danger of them catching fire. This meant keeping them away from the furnace, water heater, washer, and dryer. We chose a corner of our kitchen, where we placed a cardboard box to store neatly folded bundles of newspaper.

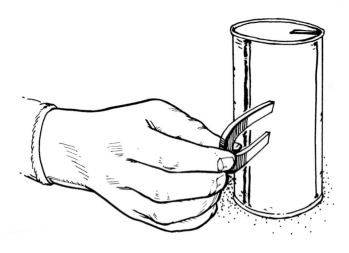

stick to it. Using a magnet is a good way to test whether a can is made of aluminum or not.

I wanted to share my books with Rosa, so I invited her over. We went into my room to read. "Look!" she said, pointing to one page. "There are other things we can do to protect the environment besides recycling."

Later that week I found some books at the library on recycling. I learned an interesting thing about aluminum: a magnet won't

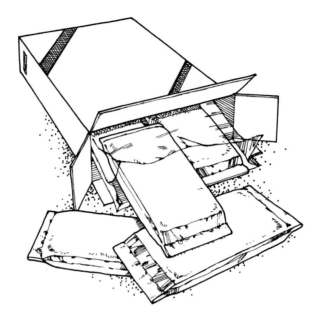

"You're right," I said, reading over her shoulder. "It says right here that we can create less trash by shopping wisely. We can avoid buying things that are only used once. This includes plastic and Styrofoam cups, plates, and containers, which can't be recycled. We can buy in large amounts whenever possible. And we can look for things that don't use fancy packaging, like extra wrappers and plastic."

"Wow!" I said, looking up from the page. "Can you believe that one-third of the average American's trash is made up of packaging that's thrown out as soon as it's opened?"

"These books are great," said Rosa. "I bet I can impress my dad with a few things *he* doesn't know.

Look at this chapter. It's about something called *compost*. It says that a lot of garbage is made up of yard waste, like grass clippings and leaves. Gee, we can use those things in the garden to create fertilizer, and we can add items from the household trash, like potato peels and apple cores. Sally, we have so much to learn and do!"

I gave her a great big
smile. "And as long as
we're trying to clean up the
planet, I might as well start
with my room!"

What Does It Mean?

automatic: able to work or act by itself

container: a holder, such as a box or jar

determine: to settle or decide

forklift: a machine that lifts and carries heavy things

furnance: a large heater

garbage: things that are thrown away

ladle: a big, deep spoon or bowl

natural resources: things we use which are taken out of the earth

organize: to plan or set up

percent: out of one hundred

pollution: dirt or waste

recycle: to make ready to be used again

rotate: to turn in circles

shred: to cut or tear into little pieces

How Do You Say It?

aluminum: uh LEW mih num

chemical: KEM ih kull

cupboard: CUH berd

cylinder: SILL in der

Fahrenheit: FAIR un hite

manufacture: man yuh FAK cher

processing: PRAH sess ing